The Buffalo and the Butterfly

Qiao Pahana

Note for Librarians: A cataloguing record for this book is available from Library and Archives
Canada at www.collectionscanada.ca/amicus/index-e.html
ISBN 1-4251-0330-8

*Printed in Victoria, BC, Canada. Printed on paper with minimum 30% recycled fibre. Trafford's print shop
runs on "green energy" from solar, wind and other environmentally-friendly power sources.*

Offices in Canada, USA, Ireland and UK
This book was published *on-demand* in cooperation with Trafford Publishing. On-demand
publishing is a unique process and service of making a book available for retail sale to the
public taking advantage of on-demand manufacturing and Internet marketing. On-demand
publishing includes promotions, retail sales, manufacturing, order fulfilment, accounting and
collecting royalties on behalf of the author.

Book sales for North America and international:
Trafford Publishing, 6E–2333 Government St.,
Victoria, BC V8T 4P4 CANADA
phone 250 383 6864 (toll-free 1 888 232 4444)
fax 250 383 6804; email to orders@trafford.com
Book sales in Europe:
Trafford Publishing (UK) Limited, 9 Park End Street, 2nd Floor
Oxford, UK OX1 1HH UNITED KINGDOM
phone 44 (0)1865 722 113 (local rate 0845 230 9601)
facsimile 44 (0)1865 722 868; info.uk@trafford.com
Order online at:
trafford.com/06-2087

10 9 8 7 6 5 4 3 2

Dedicated to absent loved ones...

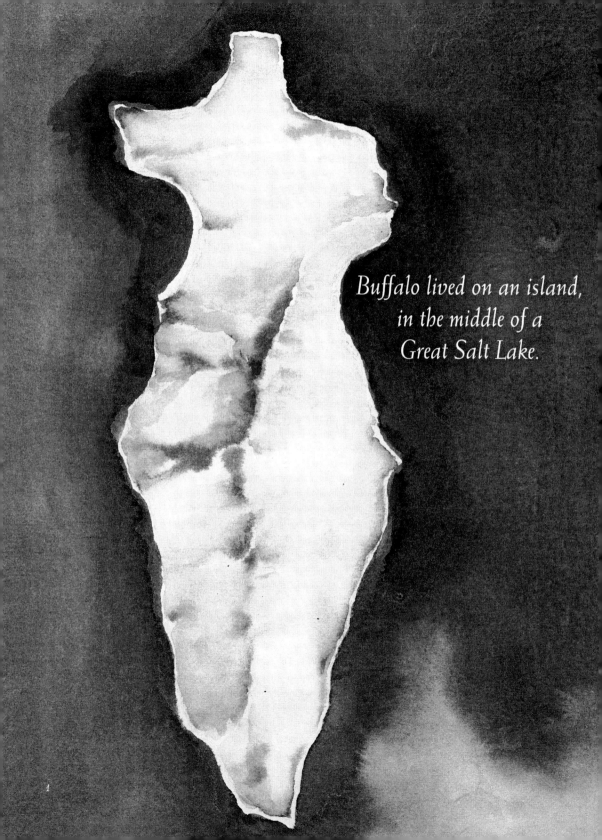

Buffalo lived on an island,
in the middle of a
Great Salt Lake.

The island was stark,
with many rocks and few trees.

Buffalo ate grass and
walked around the island,

3

And found shade in the
heat of the summer.

4

One day, a beautiful butterfly
flew past Buffalo

And landed nearby.

"Hello, Butterfly," said Buffalo, and they began to talk.

Soon they were good friends.

Buffalo loved Butterfly's
brown eyes.

9

He liked the way she moved her
colorful, bright wings,

To land on his nose, and,

Especially, to talk to him.

Butterfly loved Buffalo, too.

He was large,
and clumsy,
and sometimes
a bit smelly,

But he had a good heart.

And she knew he loved her.

Buffalo and Butterfly had many good times.

Sometimes, they would race along the beach.

Sometimes, Butterfly would play hide-and-seek in the flowers.

Sometimes they would
rest in the shade,
and watch the sun set.

20

One morning, Butterfly flew to
the highest peak on the island.

"I saw the other shore," she told Buffalo. "It had great mountains, tall trees, and lush flowers."

Buffalo shook
his head in amazement,
and admiration.

23

"You can go places I cannot go,
and see what I will never see."

Butterfly loved Buffalo, but she worried.

They were so different.

He was a big, rough buffalo,
and she was a small,
delicate butterfly,

And how could they
be happy together?

28

One afternoon, Butterfly said to Buffalo,

"We are so different, and I must move on.

Tomorrow I will fly away from this island,
across the water

To a new adventure on a new shore.
I will not see you again."

"Oh," said Buffalo, trying not to cry.

"I hope it is not because of me."

"No," said Butterfly.

"I am a butterfly, and so I wander."

"Well," said Buffalo, "It is a long and dangerous journey,

Across that lake. I hope you will be all right.

But if you must go to be happy,
then go, and I will cheer you on,

For your happiness is what means the most to me."

"But remember," said Buffalo,

"You are welcome here, and I will help you if I can,

And hear your voice in the wind,
and see your wings in every flower,

43

And feel your touch on my face with every sunset.
And I will always love you."

So the morrow came, and Butterfly spread her wings,

Flying up and away, over the many waters, until Buffalo
could no longer see her.

Even after she was gone, Buffalo looked out the entire day,

And wondered if she had made it to shore.

From that day on, Buffalo visited that place often,

Where he last saw the
Butterfly he had loved so much.

Every day he missed her,
and wondered how she was,
and prayed for her.

*He found he loved
her more than ever.*

THE END

53

ISBN 142510330-8